The *Hummel*

DRAWINGS BY BERTA HUMMEL

WITH LIGHT VERSE

ars edition

© 1984 by Verlag Ars sacra Josef Müller
All rights reserved · Printed in West Germany
ISBN: 0-86724-031-8

Originally Published:
by Verlag Ars sacra Josef Müller · Munich, W. Germany
        1939, First Printing
        1951, Second Printing
        1975, Third Printing
        1979, Fourth Printing
        1984, Fifth Printing
        1985, Sixth Printing

First Published in the United States of America
by Verlag Ars sacra Josef Müller
        1972, First English Language Printing
        1984, Second English Language Printing
        1985, Third English Language Printing

Himmel

INTRODUCTION

"Hummel" is a name familiar to everyone on the continent of Europe.

It is the signature of an artist whose work has travelled all over the world.

Her drawings crowd the windows of small village shops and big city

stores, they carry greetings from friend to friend and from land to land;

they are witty, tender, grave and symbolic. Their immense popularity has created the demand for this picture-book collection of some of her most characteristic drawings.

Berta Hummel, when she died on November 6, 1946, was a Franciscan nun, Sister M. Innocentia, living at the Convent of Siessen near Saulgau in Württemberg. It is not surprising to find an artist working within the church; monastic painters and sculptors, men as well as women, have been active throughout history. But the workroom of this Franciscan nun, which overlooked the peaceful homely fields and straggling woods around the convent, was something out of the ordinary. There, on the big table in the window, the oddest collection of shapes and figures and characters came to life in charcoal, pastels and oils; impish children, as it were, rubbing shoulders with the saints. What is the story of this exceptional woman? How did it begin?

Berta was born on May 21, 1909 in Massing-an-der-Rott in Bavaria, the third daughter of Adolf Hummel, a shopkeeper, and his wife Victoria. Three other children were born after her. There is evidence that her father's family was artistically inclined. The inscription on the gravestone of a Dominikus Hummel, who died in the year 1800, describes him as the beloved priest of his parish who was also gifted in the arts of drawing, painting and etching.

Berta went to the village school to be taught by the Catholic sisters, and from the first began to express everything she saw, in terms of line and color. Eager and impatient, already aware perhaps of what lay within her

MASSING-AN-DER-ROTT: THE MARKET

grasp, the child worked tirelessly at her drawing. She drew pictures on odd scraps of paper, on her slate, on her blackboard, on the margins of letters, and colored the pictures in all the magazines and calendars she could find. She studied the oddities of people's faces and reproduced them as caricatures, sometimes using her teachers as models!

She left the village school at the age of twelve, and for the next six years attended an Institute at Simbach-am-Inn. She learned her lessons as easily as a bird learns to fly, and the spiritual teaching she absorbed during these early years disciplined her rich nature and left its trace on her later work.

There could be no doubt about her future career, and in 1927 she became a student at the State School for Applied Arts in Munich. Here she enjoyed to the fullest all that this famous city, which has drawn artists to its bosom for centuries past, had to offer. When her studies were completed, the prize pupil of the art school decided, to everyone's astonishment, to enter the Convent of Siessen, and in August 1933 she took the veil.

SIESSEN: THE CONVENT OF THE FRANCISCAN NUNS

SISTER M. INNOCENTIA AND HOW SHE SIGNED HER PICTURES,
A SIGNATURE WHICH BECAME WORLDWIDE FAMOUS

Her decision puzzled and wounded many of her friends. No outsider can

judge the reasons for the step she took, but it must be evident that her

work and her vows were closely bound together.

Superficially her talent was many sided. She executed church decorations,

she illustrated texts and religious books, she drew hundreds of pictures

of children with profound as well as comic insight; she painted whatever she saw — the human face, the face of nature — boldly and realistically, and she expressed herself in satirical verses as well. She was in fact a mirror that reflected everything within her sight. But the mirror changed according to what it reflected and could give back images just a little larger than life.

These examples of her work are chosen to show the range of her accomplishment, a symphony as it were, of moods, carefree or contemplative, mocking or devout. If the result gives pleasure, its purpose — which is at heart an earnest one — will have been fulfilled. And so, to begin . . .

We're children in a picture book,
we hear you say: "How quaint they look,
those country clothes . . . the things they do!
Well, this is really something new."
Please join us for a little while,
we'll do our best to make you smile
and share our childish joys and woes,
we hope, as our acquaintance grows.
So now we throw the shutters wide
and bid you kindly step inside.

13

The world is mine
and I'm just five,
it suits me fine
to be alive.

I like my mother, my mother likes me,

that is the song I sing,

and that is the reason we look so alike,

it's a perfectly natural thing.

Here's a gate,
strong and stout,
it shuts you in
when you want to be out:
A gate to hate.

Here's a gate,
safe and sound,
to hide behind
where you can't be found:
A gate is great.

I'm Tom the sweep,
I'm covered with soot
from the crown of my head
to the sole of my foot.
Mark me well,
I'm not often seen,
for up-to-date sweepers
are tidy and clean.

But a dirty sweep
is worth ten of the rest,
although he's so filthy
and shabbily dressed.
Have you forgotten,
or don't you believe
that he carries luck
on his sooty sleeve?

The man behind the camera
says: "Try and look your best,
relax, don't frown, let's have a smile,
and I will do the rest."

Your neck feels stiff, your eyebrows twitch,
you want to scratch your chin.
"A smile now, please", he says again,
"and please, a wider grin."

The shutter clicks, the deed is done,
and all your troubles melt.
You hope the photograph won't look
as silly as you felt.

I've got to the top
by the skin of my teeth.
But oh! what a prospect
is stretched out beneath.

Steep as a switchback
it slopes out of sight.
But I've got to get down,
can't stay here all night.

My courage has failed me,
I'm filled with dismay,
for each of my skis
goes a different way.

Carnival and fancy dress
come but once a year,
streamers twining,
lanterns shining,
voices singing clear.

Shining lamps and glowing lanterns,
bright as stars and moons,
see them winking,
nodding, blinking,
see the gay balloons.

There's nothing more impressive than
a big, successful Business Man.
To climb the ladder of success,
it's necessary to possess
a look both stern and dignified,
an air of well-deserving pride,
a voice that makes its meaning clear
in tones that everyone can hear.
Sharp elbows are an asset too
for those who have success in view,
while all men worthy of repute
must wear a smartly tailored suit.

The theatre is crowded,
the orchestra is in,
and here is the conductor
about to begin.

The audience claps and —
with delicate poise
he raises his baton
to silence the noise.

Though outwardly calm
he's not feeling too strong . . .
For what a disaster
if something went wrong.

The music swells sweetly
as clear as a song . . .
But how they will boo him
if something goes wrong.

Lucky for him
that they can't see his face
for his back betrays nothing
but vigor and pace.

The concert is over,
they cheer loud and long,
he's a happy conductor,
for nothing went wrong.

How prettily she stands and lisps
her birthday recitation,
repeating words she learned by heart
with childish hesitation.
But who's that clown, so bored and pale,
who hangs his sleepy head?
He looks as if she didn't mean
a single word she said.

Making music is an art
that charms the ear and warms the heart.
Some find their pleasure most acute
when blowing on a tiny flute;
but sweetest notes mean greatest strain,
some players wear a look of pain,
so experts thoughtfully advise
that all concerned should close their eyes.

The waiter hurries with a tray,
the sweet looks good — ice cream today
a fitting crown to dining gay.
But conscience bids him pause, make sure
the sweet is absolutely pure
and worthy of an epicure.
One lingering taste — well, maybe two —
Yes, he decides, the sweet will do.

Man must do his duty,
from service never shrink,
and this one serves to others
what he himself can't drink.

Happy birthday, grandma dear,
on your sixty-seventh year.
Birthday presents we have brought
(four small heads and one big thought).
Vintage wine superlative,
flowers, these we gladly give,
and the cake — this lovely cake —
(how patiently we watched it bake),
what a privilege 'twould be
if we were asked to stay to tea.

By the lamp-post they're met
the male voice quartet.
First tenor sings high
almost scraping the sky,
the second, discreet,
won't try to compete,
and baritone drones
in deep fruity tones,

while bass gives a hum
like the roll of a drum.
— Each gives of his best,
but outshining the rest
proud tenor ascends
without fear, while his friends
hold the ladder of sound
firmly planted on the ground.

The infant strives with might and main
to educate his little brain.
The schoolboy stuffs his head with dates,
facts, figures, tables, measures, weights.
Then, by a miracle, the youth,
from great confusion plucks the truth
and writes a poem — only one,
for time is moving sternly on;
he finds on reaching man's estate
that poetry is out of date.

However as the stars revolve,
man finds some problem still to solve.
For instance, there's the telescope,
an instrument of endless hope
enabling him to sit and stare
and wonder what goes on up there.
Are planets peopled? Do stars move?
These things are difficult to prove.

In Paradise were flowers bright,
no child was there to take delight.
Then sorrow came to the garden fair,
and man accepted his new care.

On earth where children laugh and run
now flowers grow in heavenly sun.
When children make a daisy chain,
we know God's garden blooms again.

Adam, expelled, was forced to dig and till
the stubborn earth to do his will.
The tempest howled, the children cried,
man's curse was echoed far and wide.
But when at close of some still day
the nightingale sings in her yearning way,
man listens, mimics, softly strong,
until his heart flies home on wings of song.

"Well, puppet, speak up, state your case.
Get up. Don't lie there in your place."
"Oh doctor, help me, if you could,
for I have lost my leg of wood."

"You've lost a leg? (What rot you talk,
as if a wooden leg could walk!)
Don't waste my time. Get up, I beg,
and go straight back and find your leg."

The most absent-minded professors we've met
are those clever forgetful old fellas,
but cleverer yet are the ones who forget
that they ought to forget their umbrellas.

A cluster of children are pressed round the cot
delighted to welcome the sixth little tot.
Too bad, says the pessimist, shaking his head,
how will they all manage for clothing and bread?
Yet somehow the family's able to thrive,
while mother knows how to invent and contrive,
and brothers and sisters can each testify
that love is in full and abundant supply.

These seven valiant huntsmen
are going to catch a hare,
with spear, fork and lantern
to chase him from his lair.
If you should chance to meet him,
just tell him on the sly
these seven nervous hunters
couldn't even catch a fly.

Boots and shoes,
large and small,
old and new,
I clean them all.

Heavy clumpers — he treads dirt,
high-heeled slippers — she's a flirt.
So I judge the human race,
though I rarely see its face.

At five years old she falls in love
with a china doll called Jane,
she plants a kiss with passionate bliss
on a face that is homely and plain.

Always remember when falling in love
that fancy must play a part,
and it's sometimes wise to close your eyes
when you follow the call of your heart.

The cactus
attracts us
and distracts us.
We wonder,
is it a blunder,
that he has a nose
he never blows?

Well, you, my lad,
would be glad
if your little beak
were never known to leak.

What has the postman brought to-day?
Circulars, postcards, bills to pay,
"Mrs. Carmichael requests the pleasure . . ."
"Awaiting instructions at your leisure . . ."
Nothing, alas, in the least exciting.
But wait . . . yes, yes, it is the writing . . .
Stupid postman, can't you see
that envelope is addressed to me!

The solving of a simple sum
means argument and great debate,
but if the answer should not come
the schoolboy simply wipes the slate.

All humans err and make mistakes,
and greatest brains miscalculate,
but few corrections do they make,
their errors find them oft too late.

The knitting of socks is a difficult art,
I thought it was easy at first,
I'd gotten away to a galloping start,
and then I discovered the worst.

You knit up the leg, it's as easy as pie,
till a frightening fact you observe;
the human leg ends and the wretched thing bends,
and your needles won't go round the curve.

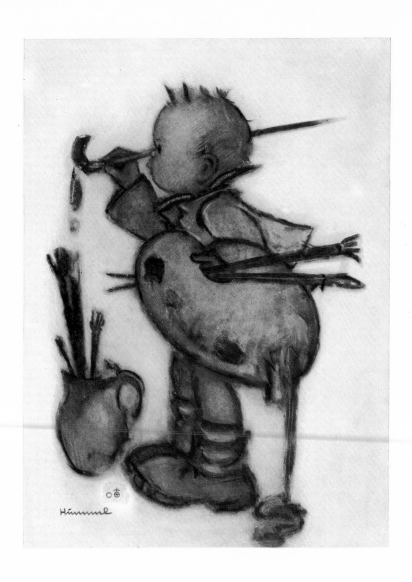

The artist dashes on the paint,
his fantasy knows no restraint,
and if the picture looks a mess
it causes him no great distress.
To make a cow look like a bus,
why, that's a sign of ge-ni-us.

The artist when he goes to view
the work that other fellows do,
will find it hard to criticize
without some envy in his eyes.
Ge-ni-us, he's apt to say,
can't be learned at school or play.

He'll read a prescription
of any description
will Timothy Tite
the dispenser.
He'll treat all your ills
with a bottle of pills,
and give you a lotion
or some other potion,
or mix you an unguent
corrective and pungent,
though whether the cure
is by any means sure
can only be guessed,
but hopes for the best,
does Timothy Tite
the dispenser.

Your tooth starts to ache, and it keeps you awake,
but you try and ignore the pain,
for the dentist's drill is more horrible still,
and the hurt you'll endure, instead of the cure,
or that's what you bravely maintain.

Then it gets bad, it's driving you mad,
so you ring at the fateful door.
In a flash it's out, you don't even shout,
and you'll never be scared any more.

How wonderful to rise and dip
upon a downy feather ship,
to glide as in a snow white dream

along a gently flowing stream.
O lovely swan, if you only knew
how much I wish that I were you.

▷
Little maidens dance and sing,
round you go in mystic ring,
like the orbits of their sphere,
like the seasons of the year,

harvest reaped and harvest sown,
angels round the heavenly throne.
Round like every joyful thing,
little maidens dance and sing.

48

Kindly repeat these words,
I pray.
"Clothes make the man? No, man makes the clothes",
I say.
You will doubtless remember, madam,
it all started with your husband, Adam.
So cover up, my friends,
come this way,
give me your orders, and don't forget
to pay.

Readers of the daily papers
very often get the vapors
when the views therein expressed
are those they heartily detest.
Some in fact are far from dumb,
their letters make the presses hum.
Here you see "Indignant Reader"
disapproving of the leader.

The baby in the garden
stares up in mute surprise,
all living things conspire
to charm his infant eyes.

The bee is gathering honey
with busy darting tongue,
the crimson-breasted robin
pours out his heart in song.

A butterfly may flicker
a moment near his bed,
the sunflower bends her petals
to shade his little head.

Deep in your cool green place crouch,
still as the flowers and the grasses,
only a dragonfly passes
restless above your hidden couch.
Tiny creature in a pigmy world
that my foot could destroy,
heedless of sorrow or joy,
existing timeless in perfection furled.

Birds on the signpost
pay it no heed,
they know where they're going,
they don't need to read.

Tramps by the wayside
stare in dismay,
words on the signpost
are all washed away.

They stand there befuddled,
the first says: "How what?"
The next says: "I'll toss you . . ."
The third says: "Oh, rot!"

The rest of the story
the picture can't show,
they may still be squabbling
for all that we know.

He blows his horn, tra-la, tra-lee,
the postman's a great fellow.
The townsfolk scurry when they see
his coach of golden yellow.

He sits as on a throne in state,
important, proud and grand,
but though he carries so much weight,
it's his at second hand.

The people push and shove and churn
to see what he has brought them,
but "Steady now and wait your turn",
is what he always taught them.

Come snow, come hail, he brings the mail,
he brought it by the packet,
that's why they cheer, they love to hear
tra-la, tra-lee, his racket.

Sky, valley, distant peaks, the morning sun
gilding the newness of a day begun,
all praise the Father's name.

O Jesus, meek and unafraid,
You speak of beauty that will never fade,
You set our hearts aflame.

Beauty of earth, the morning light,
endure forever in Your sight.

◁ They stretch, the mountain's snowy peaks
half way towards the sky,
no puny mortal bound to earth
can ever reach so high.

They sing, the children down below
upon the Sabbath day,
their thin, pure voices praising God
soar upwards endlessly.

Washing day is over,
the clothes are on the line,
all my worry's ended
provided it keeps fine.

So blow, wind, blow,
make my sheets as white as snow.
Shine out, sun,

dry my stockings every one.
Rain clouds, shoo!
I don't need any help from you.

Now shirts and pants, pajama legs,
are hanging neatly from the pegs,
I'll shout hooray for washing days
whenever the sun will show its rays.

To sweep the room   men have to search
you need a broom,   for twigs of birch
with Nature's aid   to make a broom
the broom is made,   to sweep your room.

The finest broom
won't sweep a room —
if you're asleep
the broom won't sweep;
the twigs might be
still on the tree.

The herds are plodding homeward
and day is fading fast,
the shadows gather thickly,
the light is overcast.

You hear with breathless wonder
the beat of angels' wings,
as through the friendly twilight
the distant church bell rings.

On green hilltop the wooden cross stands mute
where a shepherd boy pipes on his wooden flute,
pipes with a glad and gentle mirth
as if heaven were come to earth,
pipes little tunes of glee,
while trustful at his knee
lamb gazes up to lamb above
and all the air is filled with perfect love.

Hummel

Cheep, cheep, baby chicks,
new from the shell,
are you boys or are you girls,
how can I tell?

Eat, eat, baby chicks,
hurry up and grow,
whether you are boys or girls,
time will show.

By your deeds you'll prove your worth,
if you're cocks you'll crow,
if you're hens you'll lay me eggs —
then I'll know.

The puppy whines and whimpers,
he pleads with eloquence,
he wants to taste the cherries,
the puppy has no sense.

In vain his master scolds him,
says no, and no once more,
the puppy is insistent,
the puppy is a bore.

To maddening behavior
he has no single claim,
the conduct of some people
is very much the same.

Stepping soft with solemn faces
down the age-old forest way,
little girls are going homeward
on this sacred Easter Day.

In their arms they carry treasures,
eggs, a lamb, a banner bright,
and another, greater treasure
fills their hearts with pure delight.

The bird weary of song and flight,
buries his head within his breast
alone at the coming of night.

Happy are we who rest,
hands in loving hands,

and sleeping share

each little fret and half-remembered care
with One who understands.

When the family's hose has great holes in its toes,
I never complain, for it's perfectly plain
that sewing and mending go on without ending,
and, early or late, to darn is my fate.

The boy spells words upon the page,
the words were written by a sage.
If each one does the best he can,
then he's a fit and proper man.

"Welcome kindly evening sun,
God be praised, my work is done."
Warmed by mellow sunset beams,
the old man sits and nods and dreams,
by his side the little boy
plays a piping song of joy.

Homeward bound on weary feet,
the old woman hurries down the street,
hears the piping on the air,
feels her load less hard to bear.
"God be praised, my work is done,
Welcome kindly evening sun."

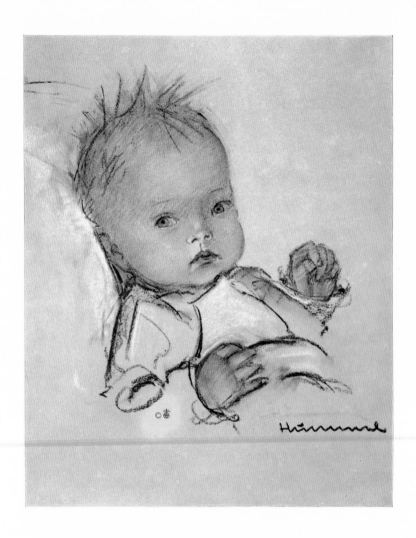

Oh baby eyes, what do you hold?
Mysteries that can't be told;
clear as water, still and deep,
you stare as in a waking sleep.
What bright visions do you see
moving in infinity?
Let no voice your rapture break,
time will come too soon to wake.

Lost in sleep,
his little limbs at rest,
the child still safely clasps
his dear doll to his breast.
And is he cherished too?
Do guardian angels keep
their wings about him pressed
while he's asleep?

Grandmother reads them the stories of old,
of princes and ladies and castles of gold.
And did it all happen, they ask, was it true?
Each fairy tale glitters and sparkles anew.

Grandfather dreams of the days that are flown,
of gallant and stirring adventures he's known,
old memories waken and sparkle anew,
he knows it all happened, yet could it be true?

Music, thou cans't inspire

the least among us with desire

to learn the ways . . .

Yet when one plays
the pleasure disappears,
and inspiration ends in tears.

She sits in sweet contentment,
her baby on her knee,
where birds make song at noonday
upon the leafless tree.

The tree has lost its foliage,
the birds will fly away,
and flowers that stud the meadow
have little time to stay.

All earthly things that flourish
have their appointed span.
May we partake, dear Father,
in Thy eternal plan.

And so good-bye, our tale is done,
we hope you've all enjoyed the fun
that helped to make this book.

We hope, if we may make so bold,
our story won't be pigeon-holed
without another look.

We hope we'll sometimes meet again,
till then . . . we cordially remain,
the children in your book.

You may wish to collect all the beautiful Hummel books
published by us.

The Hummel Friendship Book
The Hummel Thank You Book
The Hummel Get Well Book
The Hummel Birthday Book
Hummel Birthday Calendar
Hummel Address Book
Hummel Picture Diary
Hummel Art Price Guide

For the store nearest you which carries our Hummel
Line, please write us.

 inc.

70 Air Park Drive, Ronkonkoma, NY 11779